Philip Gross was born in 1952 in Delabole, Cornwall. His father was a Displaced Person from Estonia; his mother was Cornish. He is the author of several collections of poetry and also writes novels and plays. His most recent collection of poems for children, *The All-Nite Café*, was winner of the 1994 Signal Poetry Award. He lives in Bristol, where he divides his time between writing, poetry work in schools and colleges, and his own two children.

by the same author

poetry

THE ICE FACTORY
CAT'S WHISKER
THE SON OF THE DUKE OF NOWHERE
I.D.

poetry for children

MANIFOLD MANOR
THE ALL-NITE CAFE

fiction for children

THE SONG OF GAIL AND FLUDD

PHILIP GROSS   Scratch City

faber and faber
LONDON · BOSTON

First published in Great Britain in 1995
by Faber and Faber Limited
3 Queen Square London WCIN 3AU

Photoset by Wilmaset Ltd, Wirral
Printed in England by Clays Ltd, St Ives plc

A CIP record of this book
is available from the British Library.

ISBN 0–571–17535–X

10 9 8 7 6 5 4 3 2 1

Contents

Positively His Final Disappearance, 1
City Wind, 2
Touchy, 3
Skip, 4
Water Music, 6
Between Streetlamps, 7
The Doppel Gang, 8
Knucklebone Yard, 9
Shredded, 11
Man and Dog, 12
Boglady Goes to Heaven, 13
Plate Glass, 15
Guy in a Tree, 16
Witch Elder, 17
Little Acorns, 19
A Funny Turn, 20
Dodgems, 21
The Elephant Table, 23
Teatime, 1960, 24
House of Air, 25
The Song of the Song, 27
Them, 29
Joy, 31
Clangers, 33
A Window, 35
Grounded, 36
The Beautiful Boots, 37
Ring Home, 38
The Side Way Back, 39
The Prison By Night, 40
Short Stay, 41
How It Happens, 42

Mist Fisher, 43
City Litany, 44
Night Cry, 45
A Jink, 46

Positively His Final Disappearance

I bunked off.
I slipped down the crack
between Games and double Maths.
Cut round the back.

Made for the High Street
looking for a place to go.
Found myself staring
through the O

of CLOSING
smeared in the white-washed
jokeshop window. Gone:
the itching powder, stink bombs, squashed

fake spiders, vampire-, ape- and clown-
masks, plastic dog-do's for the mat . . .
All gone, no joke, except for him,
the old bloke. There he sat.

on the one chair left
on bare boards by a iron grate
and fed the fire with splinters,
smiling as it ate

its heart out. Then he turned –
all very slow,
this was – and just before he vanished,
nodded – like *so* –

as if he'd laid the whole thing on for me.
His final show.

City Wind

Not a lazy wind
  (that rather than walk round you
    goes straight through)

but an idle one,
  wind out of work,
    nothing better to do

than hang round every
  corner waiting just
    to kick dust in your eye

or scrumpling a chipwrap
  that whiffs of stale news
    before punting it high

across the street to snag
  on the fence, with tissues
    blown to shreds and a jitter

of unspooled cassette tape
  being frisked for what it knows:
    last summer's songs, the litter

of the airwaves, stripped off
  plastic, whipped round the corner
    to the Kwiksave loading bay

where the twigs and dead leaves
  gather, a nest for a season
    with no place to stay.

Touchy

'WHO D'YOU THINK YOU'RE STARING AT?'
The bomber-jacket

on a short fuse
scans the disco crush

The can in his grip
makes a hush

as it crumples. Everybody
finds a different way

to look anywhere else,
not to lock on his eyes.

'WHO D'YOU THINK YOU'RE STARING AT?'
He really needs to know.

Any moment he'll be rattling
someone like a street-collector's tin

with only coppers in it. Then
he'll nut him, drop him limp

at our feet and stare round
at a loss for an answer.

Skip

She's the one

who rattles a stick
　　on the gate where the sign
　　　　shows a Rottweiler panting
　　　　　　GO ON MAKE MY DAY;

who dials the all-night
　　phone-in, transferred
　　　　charge, and makes
　　　　　　the DJ pay;

who grins at the closed-circuit
　　cameras in colour
　　　　while the rest of us
　　　　　　are night-sight grey.

All the dogs in town are barking.
Skip says *Cool it, cool it.*
　　　　　　Come on out
　　　　　　to play.

She's the one

who leaves her name
　　on the arcade games
　　　　with a Highest Score
　　　　　　from outer space;

who just looks down the street
　　and security lights
　　　　flash on; bells shrill;
　　　　　　such an innocent face

who can sing
  I'm Too Sexy
    backwards to the tune
      of *Amazing Grace.*

All the bells in town are ringing.
Skip says *Cool it, cool it.*
          Now
          let's get out of this place.

She's the one

who gives King George VI
  a parking cone
    to keep the pigeons
      out of his hair;

who never paid yet
  on a bus or train;
    who thumbs the best
      rides at the fair;

who frisbees hubcaps
  pranged from parked cars
    high as flying saucers.
      Dare you. Double dare,

Skip says, and when they catch you
She's the one! You point
          at empty pavement.
          It was her!

Water Music

She hears the voices of underground rivers,
    a scuffle and wheeze
  like starlings nesting in the eaves,
a ringing like a shopfront full of cut glass
    trembling when a truck goes past.
      And no one else hears.

She takes the city like an outstretched hand
    and reads its palm; fine
  life- or love-lines every time
the tarmac cracks. Her footsoles take the pulse
    of buried streams. And no one else
      seems to feel; she can

and *must* tell every passer-by, time and again
    about the music. Maybe
  that's what keeps her crazy
carpet slippers shuffling (that and a drop
    of cooking sherry). When they stop
      who'll listen then?

Between Streetlamps

It's just a puddle underfoot
where the streetlight's bright.
   However high
   you pick your feet
you can't step out of it.
   It sticks.
   However quick
you stride it's in the lead,
gaining ground. Now it's a kid,
a pudgy toddler, now a teen-
   age string-bean,
a brother grown up and away.
It smears to a streak
on the pavement, till

   midway

between the lights
   it fades
like a stubbed-out smoke.
That's when – don't look –
you sense the other one,
the long pale sneak,
   at your heels.
   Walk, run –
it just breathes itself in
   and it's gone.
You're in the light, alone.
   Alone? It seeps
up through your trainer soles.
It's in the marrow of the bone.

The Doppel Gang

You think you're really someone.
Why just one? Why not two,
three, dozens out there all auditioning
to land the part of You?

Thank God for crowds; school churns,
streets seethe and cities smother.
You could live a street away and never
meet your own twin Other.

Then one day your luck begins
to spring a leak. Were you seen
by a friend of your aunt in a pinball arcade
in Clacton, where you've never been?

Did you send off to the Good News
Book Club? 'Are you feeling alright,
dear?' Mum worries. 'You don't
seem quite *yourself* tonight . . .'

There's a small ad in the paper
under Personal: a dead ringer
for you, all the details, box number
but no name, 'seeks similar . . .'

There'll be replies. They'll meet,
the envy in their eyes brewed dark and strong
behind their mirror shades. You're still
more real than them. Not for long.

One fails your exam for you. One sneaks out
to the headmaster's garage to spray
I WAS HERE, with your initials. One drives
the ambulance nobody called, as it takes you away.

Knucklebone Yard

On Bellybeast Street
you are what you eat.
Veggie burgers can't compete.
The clients arrive
from Rangerover Drive
in cars that snarl as if alive.
In Station Approach
there's a burnt-out coach.
In Hermitage Road
life's shed its load.
In Battleship Flats
there aren't even rats.
But Knucklebone Yard is the pits.

Meanwhile in the Dell
all is not well.
Air fresheners can't mask the smell,
nor sorrys and pardons
in Listeria Gardens
where new-laid concrete never hardens.
In Gazebo Crescent
they're all *terribly* pleasant.
In Plantagenet Place
it depends on your face.
Cockatiel Walk's
where money squawks
But Knucklebone Yard is the dregs.

Down Lacklustre Lane
the old people complain
and nothing is ever the same again.
Even Montague Mews
has got wind of the news
time's making an offer no one can refuse.
Chrysanthemum Court
is built like a fort;
the genteel can retire
behind barbed wire
or dye their hair mauve
in Camelot Grove.
But Knucklebone Yard is for real.

On El Alamein Way
I can't hear what you say
with lorries blasting past all day.
It's six lanes wide.
The last kid who tried
arrived fifty years early on the Other Side.
There's a mountain-bike rally
down Armpit Alley.
There's time to kill
up One Tree Hill.
And Pierrepoint Square?
Let's not talk about there.
But Knucklebone Yard is the end.

Shredded

On trashtop mountain
sheer faces of sheaves
of shredded paper hiss, hiss
in the wind like ghosts of leaves.

It's a seacliff white with droppings
and the million tiny birds
that squabble on its ledges
are the wasted words –

SCOOP *scandal* pools win GOTCHA *special offer LUCKY STARS*
used cars WE NAME THE GUILTY MEN your TV guide *Page Three*
they cry, all the agony columns . . . Huddled high
above the deaf, dumb, pulping sea

      they cry.
      Poor things, poor silly things,
      they cannot fly.

Man and Dog

They're first there when the library opens,
shuffling, snuffling, her nose to his tread.
    He stops to wheeze.
She shrugs herself down like a rug in a skip.
She stretches out across the heating vent
    and steams her fleas.

A space clears. Only he doesn't wince
at her smell. Only she could love his.
    They're last to go – where
no one knows. I saw them in the park
at dawn. She crouched, just a glance
    to check he's there.

then sleeked her ears and went swingeing
off to leave a huge dark O around him
    scuffed in the dew,
the way pigeons circle, swerving, homing
round the loft you never see, each sweep
    losing a few.

Boglady Goes to Heaven

It happened in the twinkling of her eye.

She was ever a slow, low-lying
sort of goddess, keeper of the swamp.

Ten thousand years she dozed on like the stump
of a petrified oak. Things went their ways,

seeded, rotted . . . Men lost occasional strays –
a bullock, a child – or crept near

with a sacrifice. Mostly they steered clear.
It was all the same to her, until . . . this.

She blinks. What on earth 'heaven' is
she can't imagine, but . . . Why not give it a try?

*

She floats up through several floors –
deep-pile foundations, damp-proof courses and
    Sylvan Glade aerosols can't keep her down –
up through the pampas décor of the brand-
    new shopping mall. She looks around . . .

Air-cushioned hush; ice-palace doors
that breathe souls out and in; a waft
    of unseen music; silver stairs
that lift them like gulls on an updraught
    up through waterfalls of mirrors where

each blesséd face is multiplied
a hundredfold, ascending and descending hosts
    of angels . . .

            frightful, with their empty
faces, full bags, like the souls of locusts,
    tailor's dummies of eternal plenty.

    She fights her way down and outside.
Behind the loading bay, she finds the lost
    last metre-square of naked earth
with mushed Kleenex and chip wraps as compost.
    She clings to it for all it's worth.

Plate Glass

Your humble servant . . . Tough and thin
as the sac of an egg that feels the twitch
of beak and claws within,

I'm a wall-wide tank of jewel fish
and pearly bubbles. I'm the *yes*
that money breathes soft as the swish

of limousine tyres in the rain.
Look, don't touch. Just your breath
on the glass leaves a butterfly stain.

Push and shove want to meet.
Take me! cry the goods. If I didn't keep control
they might spill out at anyone's feet.

Stress patterns too fine for the eye
to see spread like the whisper of conspiracy.
One day I'll let go, I'll let fly.

A dancer with knives, that's what I'll be.

Guy in a Tree

A crackling . . . and above my head
    there's this face in the tree
with a halo of leaves, a green mane,
    a ruff like a Spanish grandee.
'Oy, can't you read?' it said.

MEN AT WORK. KEEP CLEAR. Hard-hatted,
    roped up, clipped
on like a mountaineer, he leaned
    along the branch and stripped
the twigs off, just like that,

with a neat little hacksaw. Spring
    leaves fell like autumn. 'Mind
out!' Crash. It was a job. Hours
    later I came back to find
it done, him up there whistling

like a bird, in what had been
    a tree. It was a wicker frame,
a cage, the twigs heaped underneath
    like kindling, each leaf a flame
about to catch, to blaze with green.

Witch Elder

Old lady of the elder tree
says *Leave me be. Just leave me be.*

She's cracking up the patio.
Once she digs in she won't let go.

Her shoulder to the outhouse wall,
she mutters *Pride before a fall.*

She lets in woodlice, dampness, cold-
and-darkness you can smell like mould.

Dad asks the neighbours. They agree
(for once). Who needs an elder tree?
  (The branches whisper: *Leave me be.*)

He rips and rasps, hour after hour.
Her sap bleeds out, a yogurt-sour

thin sticky gunk. The wound stays raw
and bites back at our rusty saw

that jams, then slips and twangs and tears
Dad's wrist. Draws blood. He sweats and swears

all day. He won't come in for tea.
At last she splinters: *Leave me be.*

The wood won't burn. Splash petrol on.
It flares, twigs crunching. When it's gone

the dirty smoulder won't relight.
Smoke curdles up and stinks all night,

all next day. Half the street complains.
Try water. No good, till she deigns

to die. Don't worry, she'll be back.
Another year: green shoots will crack

her hard-scarred stump. Don't you tell me
it's superstition. This is not *our* tree.
   Let's give her space. Let's leave her be.

Little Acorns

Wriggled out of its cup
too soon,
part green, part brown,
an acorn's a shy nudist,
first time out,
pale from the waist down . . .

*

Mighty oaks from little acorns grow
– sometimes. It's a million to one,
an old trick but it might
just work. Here goes:

the long shot, all tee'd up.
Old man Autumn, the short-sighted golfer,
squints towards Spring's distant green
and blasts off . . . into the rough.

*

Hard boiled
in its roughcast eggcup
this is the breakfast
that's always gone cold.
This is the breakfast table
and the morning papers.
This is the news
that's a thousand years old.

*

A ticking bomb. Inside,
the clenched fist of an oak, the slow
explosion that can flatten houses, given time.

Slip a few in your pocket. Wherever you go
find a crack in a pavement or school wall.
Ready? Set? Now, grow!

A Funny Turn

Who didn't love Uncle Grum,
   his revolving bow tie
and his daffodil jacket? How he'd loom

into everybody's party, boneless
   stubble creasing in a grin:
Hello kiddlywinks. Guess

what I've got up me sleeve
   today? (Same tricks
whiffing of armpit). The wheeze

of his laugh. His eyes
   when the hostess, plump mother of three,
smiled and he recognised

Miss Birthday Girl
   of 1956. How everybody
beat him to his punchlines, barely

looking up from their swag
   and their gripes, never spellbound
till the day a gag

lodged in his throat. His teeth
   leaped out and landed
grinning at his feet

as if they planned on going solo.

Dodgems

It's the backs of the crowd
you can't resist. Push in
to be part of whatever it is

lights up their faces.
Dodgems!
Like bumblebees trying to swarm . . .

The music slurs.
They're fizzling to a halt
and everyone is scrambling

for a cockpit. You,
too. There are sirens,
a sizzling jolt,

some Noddycar comes slamming,
it's all you can do
with this buttery steering

to miss. Then this idiot
stalls smack in the way
and whatever you leave him screaming

gets minced
between grindstones of treble and bass,
last year's big hits.

That's when some grinning
bastard whops you. And another. And
you're making for the open

like everyone else. You just want
to get out.
And if ever you do,

if anybody asks, you'll just smile
like your grandad at the mention
of D-Day, Dunkirk or the Blitz

or films of Messerschmitts
in flames, corkscrewing
out of dizzy blue.

The Elephant Table

Grandma boot-polished them
   glistening black –
four mahogany heads
facing north, south, east, west
   with a world on their back,

a world carved out whole
   from one slice of a tree,
a world that grew old
while the Viceroy asked princes
   to treaties and tea;

in courtyards the elephants
   jewelled and penned
dozed in dust as they waited
what seemed like an age
   for the party to end.

In Grandma's dark parlour
   I crouched eye to eye
with the south-facing elephant.
Where was it looking
   so weary, and why?

And what makes me reach back
   years later to feel
little-finger-sized tusks?
Those are precious, said Grandma.
   They're real.

Teatime, 1960

Imagine listening to a brass band
while sucking a lemon.
That was Paul's mum's carpet:

several near shades of orange
fanged with neon mauve.
It snarled at the toes of the sofa.

She kept it under lock and key.
We might be allowed in at teatime
but even the Queen

would have had to take her shoes off
at the door. It was their one
brand new thing. God help us

if it didn't stay that way.
The gold-look tea trolley
bucked in the thick pile. We sat tight

on hard chairs, feet tucked up.
Paul's mum and mine talked carpets: '*so . . .
modern,*' they smiled. Then Paul

spilled a mouthful of Battenburg crumbs.
His mum was up and on him
with a scalding whisper: '*You

little heller . . . You wait.*'
He'd have bruises, shading mauve
to green, when we were gone.

House of Air

a letter was sent
but no one was there
no one at home
in the house of air

no window no frame
no number no door
between sixty eight
and sixty four

just a pit prop joist
wedged there to shore
two end walls peeling
patchwork squares

paint patterns plaster
layers on layers
unpicked by rain
and roots and years

like generations
a stray cat stirs
in the deep pile carpet
of rubble and briars

it's one big room
just follow the stairs
zig zag to the sky
through invisible floors

a fireplace smoulders
green then flares
mauve   buddleia
the postman stares

number sixty six
strange   it was there
this time yesterday
he could swear.

Post Script

'Undelivered For Reason Stated'
  – a found poem (Royal Mail)

Gone away	[ ]	Not known	[ ]
Not addressed	[ ]	Incomplete address	[ ]
Refused	[ ]	Not called for	[ ]
No answer	[ ]	Deceased	[ ]

No such street/no such place in . . .

Please tick

The Song of the Song

Boy, I was big. Big. Did I tell you?
I was Number One.
In everybody's headphones, all
that summer. Girls used to hum
me in the bath, it was me they bumped
with, every disco – well

you're only young once. It seemed
like flattery, those cover versions.
Then my agent clinched the deal –
one verse, for millions –
with the snuggest brand of jeans:
You've arrived. You'll never need

to sing again. Some techno nerds
did an instrumental – the Vienna
Phil plus drum machine. If service
stations and nine out of ten
steakhouses wanted end-
less loops of me, it just confirmed

I'd arrived. Some post-graduate
at a university not far from Oxford
did a thesis on . . . me! With my three-chord
background! I wish my old Dad
had been there. That night in the bar
they started singing me, too loud

and laughing. Laid
up in the small hours in a small hotel
I tuned in to this DJ
chirping *Time for a Golden
Oldie.* Me! I'd never played much radio.
Now I ransacked the airwaves. All night, all day

all I heard was *not-me-not-me-not-me*.
Charts. Upstarts. Dance mixes. Raps
like a slap in the face. I grabbed
a drink to drown the noise. Two. Three.
I woke with a head full of static.
Stumbled out into the street

in my stubble. No one turned an ear.
In the subway this half-alive
crusty with three strings on his guitar,
a chord-strum like kicking a bicycle,
was whingeing me at anyone who got too near.
20p in his hat. Then I knew I'd arrived.

The last verse. My friend, here we are.

Them

If you let slip a coin on the pavement
   leave it for them to pick up.
If you're drinking a tea from a takeaway booth
   leave them a sip in the cup.

     Call them the Finders and Keepers.
     Call them Invisible Friends.
     Call them a good name if any
     or . . . we all know how it ends.

Don't meet the eye of the wino.
   He might have a word in their ear.
Don't think the fact that no one invited them
   means they're not already here.

     Call them the Slow Silent Walkers.
     Call them the See-Through Folk.
     If they catch a word muttered against them
     pretend it's the next kid who spoke.

If you see someone sprawled in the subway
   don't be the first one to look.
If a beggar comes fishing for favours
   don't put yourself on his hook.

     Call them the Pale Professors
     of the University of Life.
     Don't answer back if they call you a name.
     One of them might have a knife.

Don't bother compiling statistics.
   They never keep still while you count.
They live in the margin of error
   and die an uncertain amount.

They wear out their faces so quickly.
  They pick up our old ones from skips.
They rummage our bins for words sharp and thin
  as the smile that tightens their lips.

    Scuttle home to the suburbs by sundown.
    Give certain streets a wide berth.
    Call them the Good People, call them your friends
    just in case they inherit the earth.

Joy

She's fast and foxy for you,
just you, in your sleep.
Then it's morning and the radio
is flogging old hits: *Oooh*
baby baby you're so
outa reach.

You can't imagine her
getting off the bus at Tennyson
Close or Coleridge Way
or any stop out here?
You bet she'll be down town.
With her it's Saturday

every night, it's where
you don't get in without a tie
and she'll be with this guy
who parks outside on yellow lines
and pays the fines
by cheque and doesn't care.

You pluck this slinky
BMW
and rev its heart out, two-
wheel handbrake turns that squeal
beneath you till you'd think
it's nearly her, she's nearly real,

you're nearly there
with CDs and reclining seats
and when the flashing lights
come up behind, the beat
just quickens and it's her
that rides you hard, right

up a bus-stop, and you're news.
There's sirens now,
the tick of cooling steel, a crowd
heating up, taking aim
at anything in uniform that moves,
needing someone to blame.

Clangers

Under the grumble
of the one-way system
and the tut-tut of feet
  their voices clang

      through the subway, *'Oy mister!'*
      'Look at him.' 'He fancies you!'
      like any old Saturday-afternoon
        girl-gang

just hanging out.
The shoppers hurry by,
heads down, never noticing
  what's wrong:

      no girls are there
      where old roads crossed
      and outside hallowed ground
        thieves hung,

poachers, pickpockets
and a brace of housemaids
who found their small lives
  too long

      and ran off to the city,
      swapped Mistress's teaspoons
      for a knife and learned to slit
        purse-strings

and, later, worse.
Two stray cats in an alley,
they were bagged
  and swung,

the tongues of two
cracked bells, above our heads
right here. Sing no
   sad song

but bang a dustbin lid
for them, a riot gong.
Let's make this bloody
   subway ring!

A Window

There, on the fifth floor
of a fifteen-storey
block, about twenty-
five windows (all square
and the same) along

someone is hanging
a red counterpane
out to dry. The wind
flaps it wild and free,
a flag, a kindling

flame. And whoever
she might be up there
may not dream it but
I've got the message
and, here, pass it on.

You too – so one day
the authorities
might X that spot (too
late) and say: *that's where
the whole thing started* . . .

Grounded

And now for the years
on hold
where betwixt-and-between-agers
hang out, hanging on
or simply hanging,
puppets on a playground swing
the sign says you're too old
for, but the parkie's gone.

Now for the dark,
friends' cigarette tips circling
like the wing-lights
of taxi-ing planes.
Blame air traffic control,
an invisible knot of flightpaths
(you'll never get off the ground
now) tying up the air lanes.

No one says much. Two boys
josh and scuffle vaguely. Now,
when no one's watching, you begin
to creak the swing, high, high
enough that in the moment
between rise and fall
you feel the chains go slack
and you know you could fly.

The Beautiful Boots
for Dorothy's DMs

Navvy boots
Christmas-caked, clotted
with ochre, greensand, rust, fool's gold . . .

Reptile boots
that slough scales of paint
on the carpet, new-hatched, Cretaceously old . . .

Boot boulders
speckled with bird-droppings,
blue-, black- and snow-berry, yellow chanterelles . . .

Boot icons
gilt-crusted, tarnished
and blunt as the cudgels of Byzantine bells . . .

Battle boots
fresh from kicking the daylights
out of rainbows . . . Boots stamping their ground . . .

Boot shrines
woozy with sock incense . . .
Chariots of feet that refuse to be bound

but are bound for somewhere . . . Boots to scuff
and spatter up the mud we're stuck in,
kid . . . Walk on.

Ring Home

She's come so far, what can she say?
She's punched her last coin in.
There's a pinball flicker
of connections, then the ansafone:

her mother, the voice
of her whole life so far
sounding cramped in that little
black box, speaking slow

as a hostage in the judder
of a ransom video. *Please
leave your name and your number.
Speak after the tone.*

She can't find the words to explain
to a ghost in a machine
a hundred miles away
in the hall in the house that was home.

The Side Way Back

You're late. Take a chance up the cul-de-sac,
a short cut home. It's the side way back –
the way they tell you not to go,
the way the kids and stray cats know
as Lovebite Alley, Dead Dog Lane . . .
The Council says it's got no name.

                      All the same . . .

There's sharkstooth glass on a breezeblock wall.
There's nobody near to hear if you call.
There are tetanus tips on the rusty wire.
There's a house they bricked up after the fire
spraycanned with blunt names and a thinks-balloon
full of four-letter words and a grinning moon-
                      cartoon.

It's a narrow and narrowing one way street
down to the end where the night kids meet.
You've seen the scuffed-out tips of their fags.
You've smelt something wrong in their polythene bags.
There's a snuffle and a scratching at a planked-up gate.
There's a footstep you don't hear till almost too late.
                      Don't wait.

Now you're off and you're running for years and years
with the hissing of panic like rain in your ears.
You could run till you're old, you could run till you're gone
and never get home. To slow down and walk on
is hard. Harder still is to turn
and look back. Though it's slow as a Chinese burn,
                      you'll learn.

The Prison By Night

It's like an iceberg
calved from an old slow groaner of a glacier
on the edge of arctic night –

a pale glare goes up
inside twenty-foot walls, and straight on up,
to loom there scratched by drizzle

but shedding no light
on our gardens and roofs, small craft
in a shipping lane that shrink apart

to let it through. Don't look.
You might find yourself facing a mammoth,
frost-crisped, or a leathery Neanderthal

still blinking at the news
of his own extinction. It's a fridge-door glow
at midnight, but tall as the tale

of the Castle of Glass:
how a traveller, late on the long zigzag
home, stumbled in on a fantastic party

and woke at dawn, chilled
on the hillside, to find that the night
had been years, that his family had grown,

that his friends had moved on,
and that he'd never be at home now,
not in this world or the other.

Short Stay

White lines plot the carpark tarmac
like the picture on the butcher's wall:
a cow with all the cuts marked in,
Topside, Silverside, Brisket . . .

Everybody's gone home
(though the Pay-and-Display machine
is always ready, if you've got
the money, with the time of day).

There's just this one
mud-silver family saloon.
It's irresistible:
the shadow-fingers that unpick

the seams of the afternoon
get started – first
the valve caps, then the wipers,
then the bacon-rinds of trim;

a quick hack
and the quarterlight crazes;
in the radio slot,
a few wires dangling

like the loose ends of the story:
You know Darren's dad,
he left for work one day
and he never came home . . .

How It Happens

One night's enough.
The shut shop's lights go off

for the last time. By dawn
it's done.

the window's been flypostered
over and over – some no-hoper

local band's first gig, a Socialist Worker
SMASH THE something X'd out with a swastika –

like a crumpled letter lost
years in the post

with ranks of stamps in small
denominations, all the same half-smile:

the crown prince of somewhere nobody's
heard of except quiet boys

with specs and Stanley Gibbons
catalogues, deep in the innocence

of watermarks and first-day covers
and the sound of words like *Bosnia-Herzegovina*.

Quaint name. Then it's not.
It happens. Just like that.

Mist Fisher

The rush hour steams
this winter morning,
fuming red,

red-amber, green.
Trucks grit their gears.
School buses squeal.

Dawn breathes
mist on the mirror
of the still canal

and one man (always,
only, one)
sits by the lock.

He casts a wisp
and reels in nothing
we can see

and casts again
while the lights change
and the cars nudge on.

Time leaks downstream
like peacock smears of oil,
like words you woke

repeating,
not quite understanding,
out of last night's dream.

City Litany

Hotwired on bad publicity
lowlife at high velocity
cruise canyons of immensity
with casual ferocity

each private slight propensity
pugnacity rapacity
charged up like electricity
to overload capacity

   sitcom simplicity
   public pomposity
   doubtful veracity
   wild virtuosity

   density scarcity
   mad multiplicity
   subtle atrocity
   massive complicity

      intensity
      audacity
      perplexity
      vivacity

oh city
    city
    city
    city

the end of the line   that's you

Night Cry

It might be a howl that's lost its dog

or a long skreel of brakes
before the crash that never comes

or just the way the city
sucks its breath through gritted teeth . . .

Above the iron arched station
half a million starlings rise

like dust from an explosion.
As if at a word, they bank and break

into speckling like old movie reels.
They dissolve into sky. Or reappear

like the dots of a newsprint photo
trying to compose themselves,

to be a single bird, to soar,
to roost, to fold its night-

sky wings around us. But it can't.
All over town, at parties

people pause,
mid-sentence, don't know why.

But all the rooms they're in
seem very small, beneath that cry.

A Jink

. . . a judder in the film
as if a storefront dummy
winked at you,

as if the painted backdrop
of the city slipped and what
peeped through?

A face, a grin
with teeth, like everyone's
annoying little brother

but those lines
around the eyes speak
other stories, other

centuries. You blink; he's gone.
And real life
reels on.

Other Books by Philip Gross

POETRY

Manifold Manor

'Philip Gross's *Manifold Manor* is a cut above all the single collections for children I have read in recent years. Gross is one of the most gifted of younger poets, and his inventiveness makes him an ideal children's poet.' Peter Forbes, *Listener*

'A brilliantly original collection of poems by Philip Gross, full of fun and wonder . . . This is a very special treasure trove for anyone interested in playing with words, verse forms and ideas.' Stephanie Nettell, *Guardian*

The All-Nite Café
Winner of the Signal Poetry Award

'An exciting and original poet . . . He is prepared to take risks. He challenges with rich and unusual language, and he takes his poetry for children into a territory of strong emotions, often hauntingly expressed. There is no one else writing quite as he does.' Helen Dunmore, *Poetry Review*

'An inventive and imaginatively far-reaching poet.' Michael Glover, *Financial Times*

FICTION

The Song of Gail and Fludd

'A most remarkable novel . . . a fine book, perhaps a great one.' *Junior Bookshelf*

'A brilliantly inventive variation of the rites-of-passage novel which takes all the familiar themes of the genre – the quest for personal identity, the confusing onset of sexual awareness, imaginative freedom versus institutional authority, trust, disenchantment, and the reconstitution of a shattered childhood as the pattern of adult behaviour – and wraps them up in a compulsive, surreal adventure story.' John Mole, *Times Educational Supplement*

'Not all poets are storytellers, but this one is.' *Fiction Focus*